Going for gold

Tessa Krailing

Nelson

Contents

Training for the race

It was Sports Day at Waterloo School.
Ben's Dad had come to see him run.
Ben was a good runner.
He was in the 200 metres and
he wanted to win.
Kevin was also in that race.
He was a good runner and
he wanted to win the race too.
Kevin and Ben lined up with
the other runners.
'Ready, steady, go!' shouted Mr March.
Everyone ran very quickly but
Kevin and Ben finished first.
They finished the race together.
'Well done!' shouted Mr Belter.
'Well done!' shouted Mr March.
Ben's Dad was very pleased.

5

Mr March came over to talk to
Kevin and Ben.
'You ran very well,' he said.
'I'd like you to run in a cross-country
race.
It's much longer than the 200 metres.
You would have to train for it.
You have two weeks,' said Mr March.
'So train every day and you'll be ready.'

Ben walked home with his Dad.
'What must I do to train for the race?'
he asked.
'You should do some running every day, and
we could go to the gym.'
'What would we do at the gym?' asked Ben.
'Lift weights,' said his Dad.
'If you lift weights you get fit, and
you have to be very fit for cross-country.'
'Right,' said Ben.
'That's what I'll do every day.'

Ben trained hard but Kevin didn't.
He thought he could win the race
without training.
'I'm better than Ben at running,' he thought.
'I don't have to train.
The cross-country race will be easy.
I'm bigger and stronger than Ben.
I wasn't really trying on Sports Day!'

Ben trained every day.
He went running around Wellington Square
first thing every morning.
After school, his Dad took him to the gym.
Ben lifted weights so that he would get
stronger and be really fit.
His Dad was pleased with him.
'You're doing very well,' he said.
'You should be really fit for the
cross-country race.'

A few days before the race, Kevin
was coming out of Mr Patel's shop.
He saw Ben walking back from the gym.
'What have you been doing?' he asked.
'Lifting weights,' said Ben.
'What for?' asked Kevin.
'To get fit for the cross-country race,'
said Ben.
'Are you training to get fit?'
'I AM fit,' said Kevin, walking off.
'I don't have to train.'
The only weight Kevin lifted was
a bag of crisps.

The day of the race

Soon it was the day of the race.
Mr March took the runners into the
country in the school bus.
Rocky and the other Square kids went too.
They wanted to see Ben win the race.
Just before the runners lined up, Ben's Dad
called him over.
'Remember what I told you,' he said.
'This is not like the 200 metres.
Don't run too quickly at the start.
You have a long way to go.'
'Right, Dad,' said Ben and went to line up
with the others.

Mr March waited until all the runners
were ready.
'Ready, steady, go!' he shouted.
Everyone started shouting as the race began.
'Come on, Ben!' shouted Rocky.
'The others are in front of you!'

Kevin was in front of all the
other runners.
He had started very quickly.
'Go on, Kevin!' shouted his Dad.
'You've left the others behind!'
Ben's Dad smiled to himself.
He saw that Ben remembered what he had said.
'Ben's going to be left behind!' said Rocky.
'I don't think so,' said Ben's Dad.
'If you run too quickly at the start,
you get too tired to finish.
Ben will be all right.'

Kevin was still in front of the others but
he was getting tired.
He knew that Ben was close behind.
This was a hard race.
They were only half way and Kevin was
out of breath.

Ben remembered what his Dad had said.
He wasn't running very quickly – not yet.
He wasn't out of breath and
he was catching Kevin up.
Ben could see him.
Kevin wasn't too far in front.

Soon Ben caught Kevin up.
'Hey!' shouted Kevin.
'Look what you're doing!'
You've splashed me all over.
I'm wet through!'
Ben didn't say anything.
He was saving his breath for running.
He overtook Kevin.
He was sure to win the race now!

Kevin was cross when Ben overtook him, but
he was so out of breath he had to stop.
He sat down by a gate to catch his breath.
'This is a stupid race,' he said to himself.
'Running through the country and then
round a stupid field!
Who wants to run round a field anyway?'
The other runners all overtook him, but
Kevin still wanted to win the race.

The short cut

'I know what to do!' he said, smiling
to himself.
'I'll take a short cut.
I'll run across the field, then I'll get
to the front.'
He thought no-one would see him as
the other runners had overtaken him.

Kevin got up, jumped into the field and
began to run across to the gate.
Suddenly, he heard a noise behind him.
Someone was following him across the field!
He looked behind and saw a big bull!
Now he knew why they had to run
around the field!

Kevin ran quickly.
He had to get away from the bull.
He raced over to the gate and jumped it
just as the bull had caught him up.
Kevin had been thinking about the bull and
he didn't look where he was jumping.
He ended up in some mud and he slipped and
hurt his foot.
He tried to get up but he couldn't.
His foot hurt too much.

By this time Ben had run right
round the field.
He saw Kevin sitting in the mud.
'How did you get here?' asked Ben.
'You were behind me a minute ago.'
Kevin didn't tell him he had taken
a short cut.
'I've hurt my foot,' he said.
'I slipped in the mud and I can't get up.'

'I'll give you a hand,' said Ben.
He pulled Kevin to his feet.
'Can you walk?' he asked.
'No,' said Kevin who was standing
on one foot.
'Try putting your weight on the other foot,'
said Ben.
Kevin put his foot down.
'Ow!' he screamed.
'It hurts too much when I put
my weight on it.'

'Put your weight on me,' said Ben.
They began to walk very slowly.
Kevin could see the other runners in front.
'You'd better go on or you won't
win the race,' he said.
Ben was unhappy.
He knew he wasn't going to win the race but
he couldn't go on.
Kevin's foot hurt so much he couldn't walk
without Ben's help.

'I can't leave you,' said Ben.
'You'll never get back to the
others without me.'
Kevin and Ben went on walking slowly.
Someone had already won the race.
Rocky and the others looked for
Ben and Kevin.
'Where are they?' said Rocky.
There was no sign of them.
All the other runners had finished the race,
but still there was no sign of Ben and Kevin.

Gold medal

Mr March looked at his watch.
It would be getting dark soon.
'I'm going to look for them,' he said.
He was just about to leave when Rocky
called out.
'Here they are!'
The two boys came slowly over to Mr March.
'What's happened to your foot?'
he asked Kevin.
'And why have you got mud all over you?'

'I was winning,' said Kevin.
'I would have been first if I hadn't slipped
in the mud and hurt my foot.'
Then he caught Ben's eye.
He went red in the face.
'Oh no,' thought Kevin.
'Ben knows what I did.
He knows I took a short cut.'
Kevin waited for Ben to tell the others
about the short cut.
But Ben didn't say anything.
'Ben was winning as well,' said Kevin.
'He'd have been first if he hadn't
stopped to help me.'
Still Ben didn't say anything.
He wasn't going to tell the others what
Kevin had done.

'Poor old Kevin,' said Mr Miller, his Dad.

'Does it hurt when you walk?'

'Yes,' said Kevin.

'It hurts a lot.'

'Come on,' said his Dad.

'I'll tell Mr March I'm taking you home in the car.

We'd better see to your foot as quickly as we can.'

Kevin was pleased to be going.

He didn't want to be around if Ben told the others what really happened!

Ben was still unhappy about not winning the race.

'You did the right thing,' said Ben's Dad.

'There will be other races.

You had to help Kevin.

You'll win another day.'

'He won today,' said Mr March.

Ben and his Dad looked surprised.

Ben hadn't won.

He and Kevin had come last!

'Come with me,' said Mr March.

Mr March gave a cup to the runner
who had come first.
But Mr March said that wasn't all.
'Someone here today showed that he was
a really good sport.
He didn't win the race because he stopped
to help someone.
That was the right thing to do.'

Mr March called Ben over.
'Ten years ago I won a gold medal.
I won it running for my country.
Now I would like you to have it.'
He gave Ben the gold medal.
Ben didn't know what to say.

Kevin was on his way home in his Dad's car.
His foot hurt, he had mud all over him,
he had to run away from a bull and
he hadn't won the race!
It hadn't been a very good day at all!
Ben went home in the school bus.
He was very pleased with his medal.
He might not have won the race, but
he had helped Kevin and everyone was
pleased with him.
It was better than winning the race!
Well, almost!